Written by Tony Bradman

Illustrated by Dylan Gibson

Hachette UK's policy is to use papers that are natural, renewable and recyclable products and made from wood grown in well-managed forests and other controlled sources. The logging and manufacturing processes are expected to conform to the environmental regulations of the country of origin.

ISBN: 9781398324244

First published in 2022 by Hodder & Stoughton Limited (for its Rising Stars imprint, part of the Hodder Education Group),
An Hachette UK Company
Carmelite House, 50 Victoria Embankment, London EC4Y 0DZ

www.risingstars-uk.com

Impression number 10 9 8 7 6 5 4 3 2 1
Year 2026 2025 2024 2023 2022

Author: Tony Bradman
Series Editor: Tony Bradman
Commissioning Editor: Hamish Baxter
Educational Reviewer: Helen Marron
Illustrator: Dylan Gibson
Design: Helen Townson
Page layout: Stephanie White/Kamae Design Ltd
Editor: Amy Tyrer

With thanks to the schools that took part in the development of Reading Planet KS2, including: Ancaster CE Primary School, Ancaster; Downsway Primary School, Reading; Ferry Lane Primary School, London; Foxborough Primary School, Slough; Griffin Park Primary School, Blackburn; St Barnabas CE First & Middle School, Pershore; Tranmoor Primary School, Doncaster; and Wilton CE Primary School, Wilton.

A catalogue record for this title is available from the British Library.

Printed in India.

Orders: Please contact Hachette UK Distribution, Hely Hutchinson Centre, Milton Road, Didcot, Oxfordshire, OX11 7HH.
Telephone: (44) 01235 400555. Email: primary@hachette.co.uk

Previously in Forbidden Classroom ...

Inbox > New message

TO: SENTINELS HQ

AGENTS: RIPLEY AND ARNIE

REPORTING IN FROM: ROCKHEAD PRIMARY SCHOOL

Yesterday, a power surge in the portal was followed by the arrival of The Intruder – an alien robot.

Purpose of The Intruder's mission: information gathering to make an alien invasion easier.

Methods used: mind control, seizure of school Wi-Fi.

Response: Agents Arnie and Ripley took action. New agents Verna Lee and Jamie Ballard defeated The Intruder, then sent it back into the portal.

Awaiting science team and further instructions …

PROLOGUE
Things are definitely changing at Rockhead Primary ...
... the school isn't usually this busy in the middle of the night ...
But now it's the most important place in the world.
HUMMMMMMM ...

It's not very impressive, is it? I was expecting it to be, well, a lot more ...
Alien? Me too. It hasn't been active since The Intruder incident, either.
Are you sure about that, Torres? We'd better check the most recent data.
There you go, Hopper ... no change.
Hold on ... something is happening ...
It looks like the school is about to get even busier!
BZZZZTTTT ...
ZZZZZZZPPP
Whoa ... we'd better let HQ know!

Several hours later ...
What's all this about? Why are these soldiers here?
Mrs Sharma explained everything in her email, Mum. Didn't you read it?
We just need a bit of extra security. You know, because of the portal ...
A bit? That looks like a whole army. Is it safe for you to go in?
Don't worry, Mum. I'll keep my head down if anything dangerous happens.
Very funny. Just make sure you don't upset your teacher. See you ...
It's fine, Dad. You never know, I might even learn something interesting today.
Well, I certainly hope so. Anyway, I'll be off ... have a good day!
CHUPPA-CHUPPA-CHUPPA-CHUPPA-CHUPPA ...
This is so cool. I never thought I'd see anything like it at Rockhead!
I can't wait to meet the science team. I've got so much to tell them.

... CHUPPA-CHUPPA-CHUPPA-CHUPPA-CHUPPA-CHUPPA ...
Hang on ... it looks like that helicopter is heading in our direction!
It is, and it's going to land ...
... IN THE PLAYGROUND!

... CHUPPA-CHUPPA-
CHUPPA-CHUPPA-CHUPPA ...
AREA IS SECURE, MA'AM! YOU ARE NOW CLEAR TO EXIT FROM THE CHOPPER!
... CHUPPA-CHUPPA-CHUPPA-
CHUPPA-CHUPPA ...
SCHOOL ENTRANCE TWENTY METRES IN A NORTHERLY DIRECTION, MA'AM!
... CHUPPA-CHUPPA-CHUPPA-
CHUPPA-CHUPPA ...
OK ... let's get this done. With me, Blake and Riggs ...

... CHUPPA-CHUPPA-CHUPPA-
CHUPPA-CHUPPA ...
COME ON! THIS COULD BE INTERESTING ...
I'm afraid school rules don't allow helicopter landings in the playground, so please make sure you don't do that again! Anyway, welcome to Rockhead. How may I help you today?
Where is the headteacher's office?
Er ... it's over there. Mrs Sharma is very busy at the moment, so she won't be able to see you till later. Hold on, what do you think you're doing? You can't just walk into her office ...
I think she just did.

Excuse me, who are you? It's very rude to just barge in like that. We're having an important meeting.
I did tell her she'd have to wait, Mrs Sharma, but she wouldn't listen.

I don't have time to wait. Not when the future of the world is at stake.
Pssst! It's Director Keller, our boss. The science team sent for her.
Oh, right, I see. Well then, I suppose we should talk. Don't worry, Mrs Jones. I'll take it from here.

Talk? I'm here to take control. I'll need an office while I'm here, of course. This one will do nicely. You'll have to move out and find somewhere else, Ms ... what is your name?

Sharma. My name is Mrs Sharma. And what exactly do you mean by 'take control'?

Oh, don't worry, I won't be running the school for you. That's your job. I can't stand kids, and I'd like you to keep them out of the way while I do my job. I'm just here to save the world.
I don't see why you need my office. I'm sure we could set something up for you.

Let's just say it will be easier for everyone ... if you do as I ask.

Well ... I'll see what I can do. In return, I'd like you to promise there won't be any damage to my building.
I don't make promises I can't keep. None of this should be happening, anyway. We had people here who were supposed to make sure the portal stayed hidden. That was YOUR job, Arnold and Ripley.

I know we've let you down, Director Keller, but ...
I don't want to hear your excuses. You have both failed in your mission, so you can both stand down. Blake and Riggs will take over the Control Centre with immediate effect.

Hey, you can't do that, it's not fair! Arnie and Ripley did their best.
Is that right? Well, their best wasn't good enough. And who are you?

Er ... this is Verna Lee and Jamie Ballard, Director, the two children I made into Junior Sentinels. I mentioned it in the report I sent you.
Well, it was a crazy idea to have kids as Sentinels. Hand over your badges, all of you. And stay away from The Forbidden Classroom.

Do as she says, kids. You too, Ripley.
Fine. I was going to quit anyway.

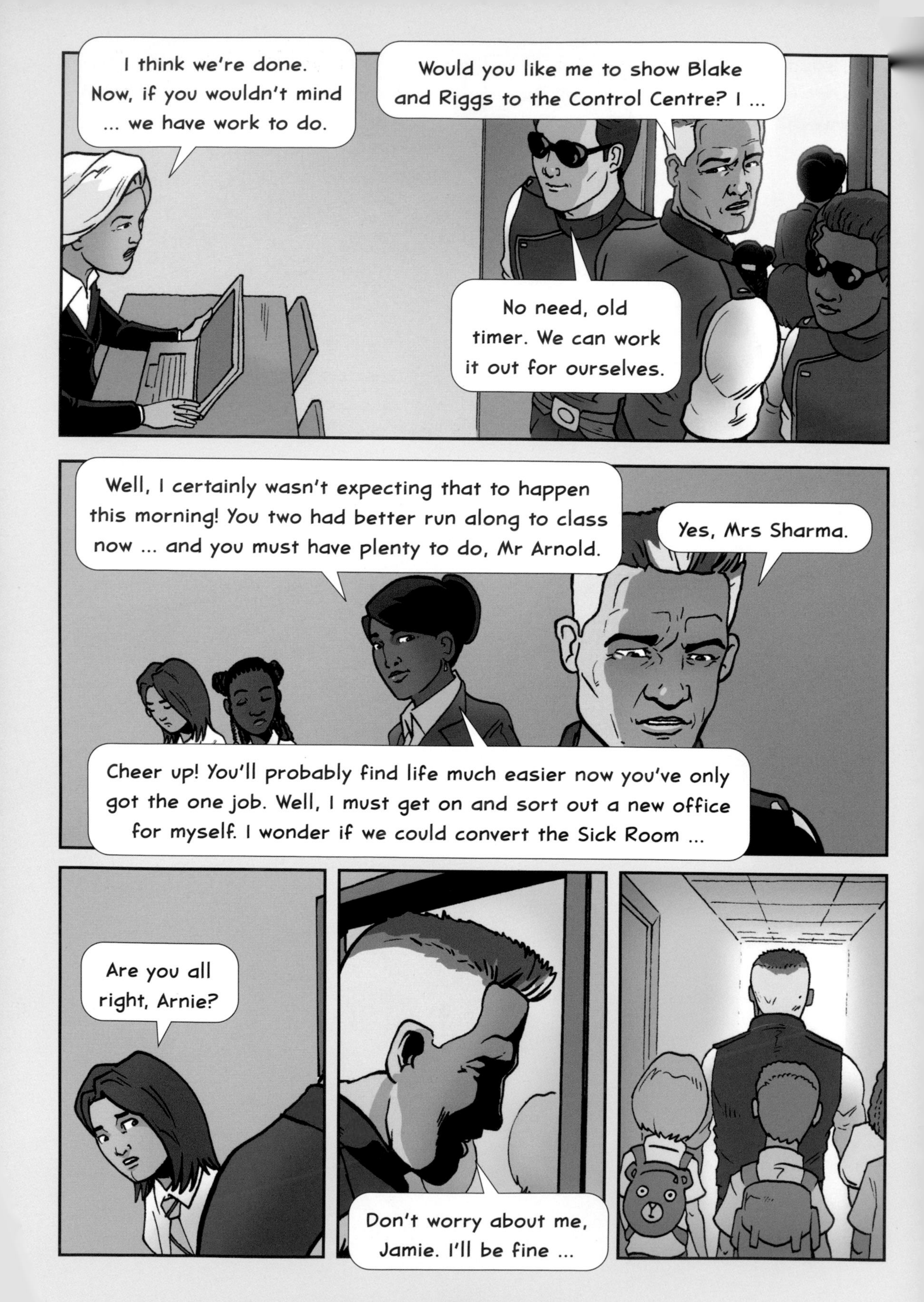
I think we're done. Now, if you wouldn't mind ... we have work to do.
Would you like me to show Blake and Riggs to the Control Centre? I ...
No need, old timer. We can work it out for ourselves.
Well, I certainly wasn't expecting that to happen this morning! You two had better run along to class now ... and you must have plenty to do, Mr Arnold.
Yes, Mrs Sharma.
Cheer up! You'll probably find life much easier now you've only got the one job. Well, I must get on and sort out a new office for myself. I wonder if we could convert the Sick Room ...
Are you all right, Arnie?
Don't worry about me, Jamie. I'll be fine ...

So I suppose that's it, then. We're back to just being bored school kids.

Only if we do what the grown-ups say, and I'm not very good at that.

Me neither. I'd really like to find out what the science team is up to ...

OK then ... follow me! We'll need to get past Mr Wiley and Mrs Lamont without them seeing us ...

Hey, where do you think you're going? Kids aren't allowed in there.

We have an important message for the science team. From Director Keller.
You should have said that in the first place. No problem. Step right in.
HUMMMMMMMMMM ...
BZZZZZZZTT!
ZZZZZZZZPPPPTT!
Wow, I'm very impressed! They've got some amazing equipment.
I'll take your word for it. Let's find out what's happening ...
How fascinating. When did the level of space radiation start rising?
At precisely 5:17 this morning. It rose steadily for a while ...
... But now it's rising much more quickly, and that means ...

The portal is about to open.
Yes, you're probably right.
I agree ... hang on, who are you?
I'm Jamie, and this is Verna. We've seen the portal open before, so if there's anything you want to know, just ask.
Really? Well, I did wonder how high the radiation level usually gets to before it opens? It seems to go up and then ...
What are you doing, Hopper? These are just kids! They shouldn't be in here – and we shouldn't be talking to them!
Well, it's getting pretty close to the level we saw last time ... and now it's there! I'd say the portal will open any second ...

CRACCCKKKKLLLE!
ZZZZZZPPPPPTTTTT!
... NOW!
BZZZZZZZTTTTTT!
ZAP-POW!
WHOOP-WHOOP-WHOOP!
Something is coming through!
Maybe it's the robot again ...
It definitely isn't.

Hail, Earthlings!
I come in peace ...

... So please put those guns down before somebody gets hurt.
Hold your fire, everyone!
Er ... welcome to Earth. And you are ...
I am MURLAK, servant of His Incredible Highness, Emperor Kalgorr of the Veem!
That's all very well. But was it you lot who sent a robot through the portal?
It was. We wondered if there had been a problem. It was badly damaged when it returned.
I'm glad to hear it. Your robot caused a lot of trouble while it was here.
It also said you were planning to invade and take us over. Is that true?

No, it is most definitely NOT true! Our robot must have been affected by space radiation on its journey from our planet.
Really? It seemed to be working pretty well. It knew what it was doing, too. Where exactly is your planet, by the way? And what are you ...

Right, that's enough, you kids really shouldn't be here. I'm sure our guest doesn't want to be pestered by you ...

OK, what's going on? Hopper? Torres?
I am so sorry, Director Keller, we were about to send someone to tell you ...
... That we have a, er ... visitor. We've just been asking him some questions.
Hey, we aske
questions,

And very interesting questions they were too. I need to speak with whoever is in charge. I have an offer for you Earthlings.
I'm in charge, so speak to me. Er ... what kind of offer?
I'd rather not say here. Can we go somewhere more ... private?
Of course. Come to my office.
Hang on, he seems a bit shifty to me. I don't think you should trust him. Not till we know more.
Not you two again! You were told to stay out of here. Blake, Riggs – remove these kids. Now!

Yes, Ma'am!
Move it, you two.
OK, OK – we're going. But don't say we didn't warn you!
This way, please, er ... Mr Murlak.
Thank you. Oh, and it was good to meet you, Verna Lee and Jamie Ballard.
I don't remember telling him our names.
Nobody else in there used them either.
That's strange. It's almost as if he ...

... Was telling us he knows who we are. Yeah, I thought that too.

But how does he know? I thought we destroyed all the data the robot collected before we sent it back.

It looks like maybe we didn't. I'm sure this Murlak is up to something ... We just need to find out what.

We should ask Arnie and Ripley what they think. I can't believe they're going to give in to this Keller person.

Me neither. Come on, I'll bet they're down there working out a way of making Keller give them their jobs back.

Sorry, kids, it really is over.

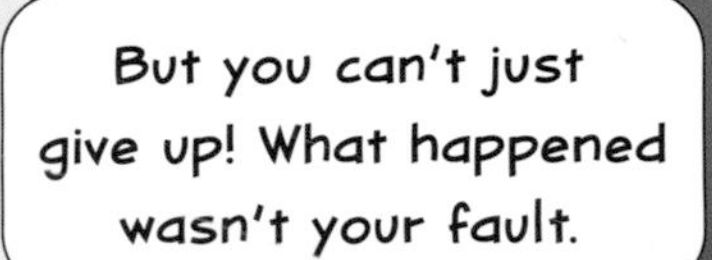
But you can't just give up! What happened wasn't your fault.

Nice of you to say, Jamie. But I failed, and I have to take the blame.

What about Ripley? She doesn't think you failed, or that she did either.

You got that right. But there's no point arguing with someone like Keller.

We have to get her to listen to us, though. There's a new threat.

An alien called Murlak has come through the portal, and Keller is talking to him right now. We think he's up to something.

Really? Umm, that's very interesting. What do you think, Arnie?

I think ... that it's not our business any more. Forget it, Ripley.

That's good advice, Ripley. I'd take it if I were you.

We'll take over in here now, thanks.
We were just leaving.
Hey, hold on a second, we might need you to explain how some of this equipment works. It's all so old.
Sure, no problem.
Work it out for yourselves. Come on, Arnie – let's get out of here.

Is he going to be OK? We're worried about him.
Me too. But he's tough. He'll get through this.
But what about Murlak? You believe us, don't you, Ripley?
Maybe. It sounds like we should keep an eye on him, anyway ...
We can't have anyone causing mischief here at Rockhead Primary, can we?

We need to find out what Murlak is saying to Keller.
I'm guessing they're still in Mrs Sharma's office.
We can't hear them from here. We'll have to go outside.
No, I'm sorry, I'm afraid you'll just have to move some of your tanks. We need access to the playground at all times. What if there was an emergency, a fire or something?
Come on, this way!
Good, the window is open.

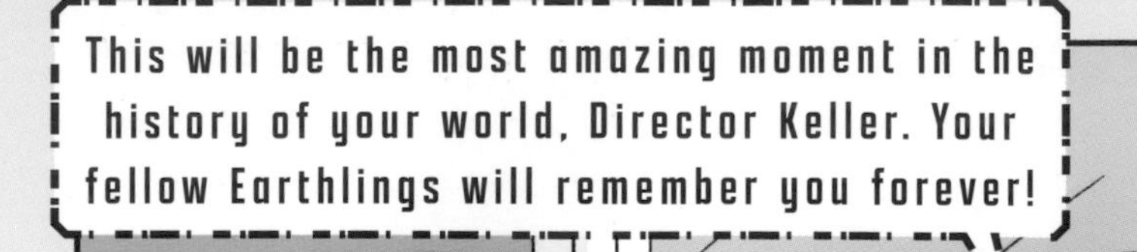
This will be the most amazing moment in the history of your world, Director Keller. Your fellow Earthlings will remember you forever!
I know. But you're part of my success too. Thanks to your generous offer, our world will be much better in the future. When can you start bringing everything through the portal?
Hey, what are you kids up to?
Quick, run for it!

Shall I go after them, Director?
No, they're nothing to worry about.
Umm, I'm not so sure. But we can deal with them later ...

I don't like the idea of Murlak bringing something in through the portal.
It won't be good, whatever it is. But he's certainly got Keller fooled.
I'll bet he just kept telling her how wonderful she is. She's very big-headed. So, what's the plan?
Same as ever – keep our eyes peeled, and just find out as much as we can.
Ah, good to see you, Jamie and Verna. I know being in class isn't as exciting as being a Sentinel, but I'm sure we can still teach you something.
Haven't you heard, Miss? We've been chucked out of the Sentinels, along with Mr Arnold and Mrs Ripley.
Mrs Sharma has been chucked out of her office too, and the day has hardly begun! It makes you wonder what will happen next.
I think we're about to find out.

Please Miss, Mrs Sharma says there's going to be a Special Assembly. Director Keller of The Sentinels wants to talk to everybody. I've actually met her!
It's all so exciting! An alien has arrived and he's going to talk to the whole school as well!
Thanks, Zofia and Kane. Right, stop what you're doing, everyone, and start lining up ...

I think Director Keller is so cool ...

Well, I'm not impressed. Did Mrs Sharma say any more about the assembly?

Not much. She was a bit grumpy. I don't think she likes her new office.

Come on everyone, you know Mrs Sharma doesn't like to be kept waiting.

Good morning, children.
Good morning, Mrs Sharma. Good morning, everyone.
So where is Murlak, then?
Oh, I'm sure he'll turn up ...
We have some, er ... important visitors with us today, and they have a rather, er ... important announcement to make. So I'll hand over to Director Keller of The Sentinels now. Please make sure you give her a proper Rockhead Primary welcome.
Thank you, Mrs, er ... Mrs ...
Sharma. It's S-H-A-R-M-A. Mrs Sharma.
Whatever. Well, er ... good morning, children. I'm here to tell you ...

Good morning, Director Keller. Good morning, every ...
SILENCE! I do the talking. All you kiddies have to do is LISTEN ...

She'll be lucky. I've been trying to get my class to listen to me for years.

Sorry? Did you say something?

... It isn't every day that you get to meet someone as important as me. But today you also get to meet someone who is almost as important as me, and who will help me change the world ...

Prepare yourselves to meet an alien from another galaxy. I asked him to stay out of sight till I thought you were ready. I know you kiddies get scared easily. You can come out now, Murlak.

He's not very scary!
Ssshhh! Don't be so rude, Kane! I'm really sorry, Mr, er ... Murlak.
No need to apologise ...
I took it as a compliment. But I can be scary if you want ... RRROOOOAAARRR!
Just kidding! They're not as easily scared as you thought, Director Keller. I'll have to try harder next time.
I wonder if that's a promise or ...
... A threat? It might be both.

But Director Keller is right. I am from another galaxy. My species is called the Veem, and we seek out other species who are not as advanced as us. We help them to solve their problems and make their worlds better. And that is what we will do for you Earthlings. Let me show you …
We will bring our technology to your planet through the portal and show you how it works. Then you can use it …
… to make your world perfect.

Thank you, Murlak. I think the people of Earth will be very grateful to you, and to me of course. Now I just want to ...
Excuse me, can I ask a question?
No, you can't. Now, as I was saying ...
Of course you can, Jamie. I have some questions I want to ask as well.
I was wondering what's in it for you. I mean, why do you want to help us?
Ah, Jamie, that's easy. What we do to other species makes us feel good.
But ...

OK, kid, one question is enough. We haven't got time for any more. The new technology will start coming through the first portal any time soon. And we'll be very busy once the new portals open.
I'm sorry, what did you say? Nobody told me about any new portals.
I don't want them here any more than you do. I'd rather have them at Sentinels HQ, but it seems that isn't possible. Murlak says he needs four more portals, and they have to be in your school.
My apologies, Mrs Sharma. More portals means we can help you more quickly, and this is the best place for them. I could explain why, but you wouldn't understand…
I would! It's all to do with ...
You can explain it to me later, Verna. But I think Director Keller, Mr Murlak and I need to talk in private ... right now. This Special Assembly is over, so you can all return to your classrooms.

How dare you arrange something like that without my permission! We'll need to do a health and safety check at least ...
I want a flying car when I grow up.
You know, I was thinking of giving up being a teacher. But if the school is going to get some new alien gadgets I might stay on!
I want to be like Director Keller.
Why on Earth are you wearing sunglasses, Zofia? Take them off before you trip over and do yourself some damage!
Murlak has fooled everyone else too. I can't believe they fell for all that.
He didn't fool me. You kids were right. This Murlak is definitely a problem.
The question is – what do we do now?
I think we should talk to Mrs Sharma.

BBBRRRMMM ...
But there must be something you can do, Mrs Sharma. We have to stop Murlak before it's too late!
VVVROOOMMM, VVVROOOMMM!
I agree. The idea of having even more of these dreadful portals in my school is absolutely the last straw. But I'm not sure there's much I can do. Besides, I'm not terribly worried about Murlak. If he causes any trouble all those soldiers should be able to deal with it.
That's true – if they're still around. But it looks like they're leaving.
We'd better find out what's going on!
BBBRRRMMM ... VVVROOOMMM, VVVROOOMMM!
Hey, why are you all leaving?
Orders from Director Keller!

BBBRRRMMM ...
VVVROOOMMM, VVVROOOMMM!
There you go, Murlak. I've ordered my troops to leave, as you asked. You're right, we need to trust each other. This could be the beginning of a beautiful friendship between our worlds.
Thank you, Director Keller. I'm sure you won't have any reason to regret what you're doing. Please excuse me ...
... I have to ensure everything is ready for the opening of the new portals.
Hold on, Mr Murlak, I want to talk to you about these new portals ...
I'd like to find out more about the new portals too. But for that we'll need access to some special equipment.
Are you coming with us, Ripley?
No, I thought I might check on Arnie. Keep me posted ...

HUMMMMMMMMM ...
Those scientists weren't very friendly last time. They might not let you use their equipment.
BZZZZZZTT!
ZZZZZZZPPPPTT!
Don't worry. I can handle them.
You're wrong, Torres, the data shows that the levels are rising!
No, you're the one who's wrong, Hopper. The data shows the opposite ...
Er, excuse me. Perhaps I could help?
Oh, no, not you two kids again! You know you're not allowed to be in here.
Be quiet, Torres. We need all the help we can get. Over to you, kid.
Thanks. Umm, this is fascinating ...

The levels are definitely rising ... You could do all sorts of things with that much space radiation. It's more than enough to open one ... two ... three ... four more portals ...
... and it should happen some time just after lunch.
Whoa ... it looks as if it's going to be pretty spectacular.
I wonder if we should get Mrs Sharma to evacuate the school.
Really? Do you think we're in danger? Director Keller said ...
Director Keller says a lot of things. Evacuation is a good idea.

Sending the whole school on a trip to a museum is a great idea, Mrs Sharma.
Yes, at least they'll all be safe if something terrible does happen.
They might even learn something too. I didn't want them all thinking I was just giving everyone the afternoon off. Especially the teachers.
ZZZZZAAAAAPPPPP!
CCCCCRRRACCCKKKLLE!
ZZZZPPPPTT!
Looks like there's a storm coming.
Yeah, an alien one. Come on ...
... We need to find Murlak.

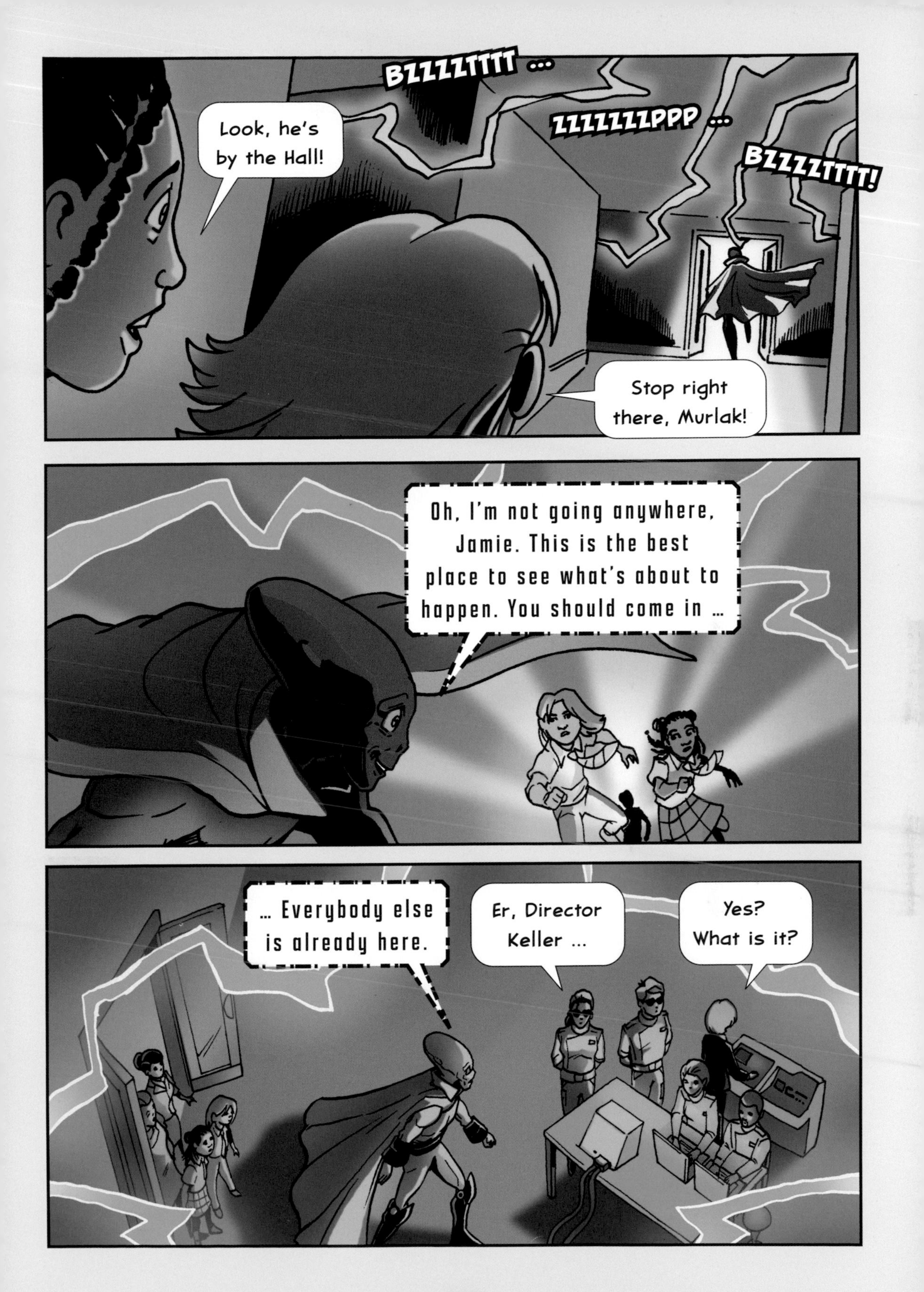
BZZZZTTTT …
Look, he's by the Hall!
ZZZZZZZPPP …
BZZZZTTTT!
Stop right there, Murlak!
Oh, I'm not going anywhere, Jamie. This is the best place to see what's about to happen. You should come in …
… Everybody else is already here.
Er, Director Keller …
Yes? What is it?

Radiation is reaching a critical level.
I see ... how soon will they ...

Portals opening in ten seconds, nine, eight, seven, six, five, four, three, two, one ...

... ZERO!
ZZZAAAPPPP!
PPPPOOOOWWWW!
CCCCRRRRAASSSSH!

BBBBOOOOMMMM!
TINKLE, TINKLE ...
ZZZZAAAAPPP!

Come on, let's have a look!
Mrs Cradock isn't going to be happy when she sees what's happened to her Library.
Umm, interesting ... it's more stable than the first portal. And the energy doesn't seem to be fading.
Er ... I don't think you should get quite so close to it, Verna.
Jamie's right, Verna. I need you to step away from the portal ...

I see what you mean!

Uh-oh. It was bad enough when there was only one of these things.
Yeah, I still have nightmares about it. Let's get out of here ...

THUD, THUD, THUD, THUD, THUD ...

THUD, THUD, THUD, THUD, THUD ...

Ah, thank you for leading them to me, Jamie and Verna. Very good of you.
You didn't say anything about robots bringing your technology, Murlak. We know how dangerous just one of them can be. This many could cause a lot of trouble.
Quiet, kid. Murlak told me the robots were coming – they're nothing to worry about. They don't have any brains, they just obey orders. Like Blake and Riggs.

??

I might have told a few fibs, actually. You should definitely worry about the robots. The technology isn't quite what I said it would be, either ...

It turns into the most powerful weapon in the galaxy. The truth is that I *was* sent here to conquer your planet. And I will DESTROY anyone who tries to stop me…
SSSSMMMMAAAASSSSHHHH!
We're all going to die!

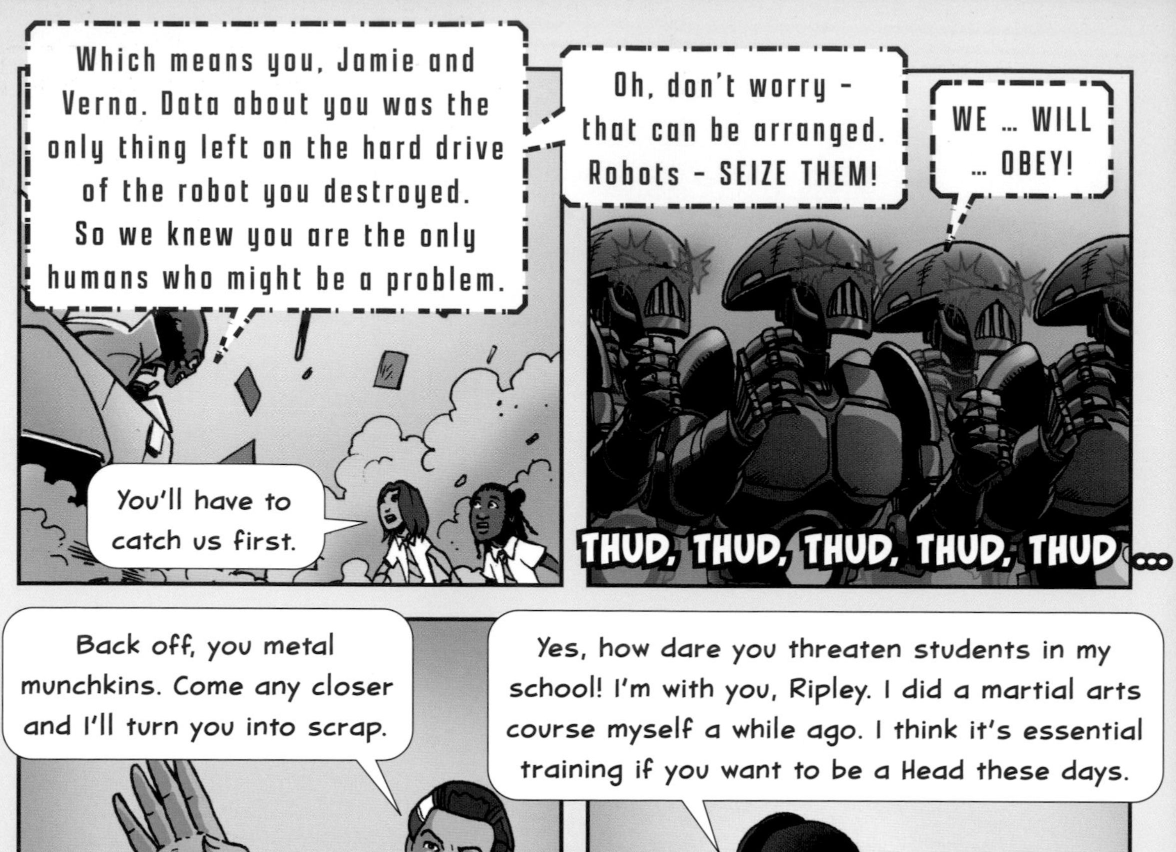
Which means you, Jamie and Verna. Data about you was the only thing left on the hard drive of the robot you destroyed. So we knew you are the only humans who might be a problem.
You'll have to catch us first.
Oh, don't worry – that can be arranged. Robots – SEIZE THEM!
WE … WILL … OBEY!
THUD, THUD, THUD, THUD, THUD …

Back off, you metal munchkins. Come any closer and I'll turn you into scrap.

Yes, how dare you threaten students in my school! I'm with you, Ripley. I did a martial arts course myself a while ago. I think it's essential training if you want to be a Head these days.

Outstanding, Mrs Sharma! I just wish Arnie was here to help us, too.

I wouldn't miss this for the world.
Thank goodness you're here, Arnie! I know we'll beat Murlak now.
Thanks, Jamie. But we'll need more than just me to win this battle.
I do have an idea, as it happens ...
Er ... I hate to break up the touching reunion, Arnie, but you're needed ...
You kids go and save us all. We'll keep the bad guys here as long as we can.
CLANNNNGGGG!
CLUNK!
POW!
CLANNNNGGGGG!
WALLOP!
OK, we need to get to The Forbidden Classroom. And I need you to come with us, Hopper – it's our only chance.
POW!
No problem. What's your plan?
I'll tell you when we get there.

Awesome combat skills, Arnold.
Oh yeah ... Can we join in too?
What about your boss? Maybe you should ask her permission first!
She's not our boss any more.
Good to hear. OK, then ...
ZZZAAAPPP!
ZZZAAAPPP!
ZZZAAAPPP!
... Let's get to work.
Stop! There's no escape!
That Murlak is full of surprises.
WWWWHHHHOOOOSSSSSHHHH!
Follow me! He's after Jamie and Verna ...

I won't miss next time.
ZZZAAAPPP!
ZZZAAAPPP!
BOOOMMMMM!
ZZZAAAPPP!
ZZZAAAPPP!
Quick, in here!
ZZZAAAPPP!
Whoa. Now that's some portal.

My plan is simple. If we can reverse the energy flow of the portals they might suck Murlak and the robots back to where they came from. We'll all be safe because we haven't been exposed to space radiation.
That's brilliant! The first portal seems to be the one that controls the others. We just need to connect to it.

Er ... could you hurry up? I don't think we've got much time.

WWWWWWHHHHHHOOOOOOOSSSSSSSHHHHHH ...

Right, here we go ...

Well, this has all been a lot of fun, but I'm afraid I need to get on with conquering your planet. So ...
RRRRRRIIIIIIPPPPP!
... It's time we said goodbye.
CLICK!
CLICK!
CLICK!
Do it, Verna!
BBBBZZZZTTTT ...
CLUNK!
???
ZZZZPPPPTTTT ...

BBBBZZZZZTTTTT!
ZZZZPPPPPTTTT!
SSSSSQQQQUUUUUEEEEEE ...
SCRRRAAAAPPPPE!
CLANG!
BANG!
Nooooooooooooooooooooooooooo ...
CCCLLLAAANNNGGG!
BBBBZZZZZTTTTT!
ZZZZPPPPPTTTT!
BBBBZZZZZTTTTT!
ZZZZPPPPPTTTT!
POPPPP!

You kids OK? Where are the bad guys?
We're fine, Arnie. Verna got rid of them. It was the coolest thing ever!
Well done, Verna and Jamie! You'll definitely be getting good reports from me at the end of the year. But I'll have to contact your organisation, Mr Arnold. Someone has got to pay for all this damage to be put right.
I'm just hoping that's the last we've seen of Murlak and his robot pals.
I wouldn't count on it.
Neither would I ...
BBBBZZZZTTTT!!!!!

EPILOGUE
Not so long ago Mrs Sharma was just a Headteacher ...
I'm sorry, but I haven't got time to answer any more questions, I'm afraid. I do have a school to run, you know, and we have a lot of work to get it ready for the children to return tomorrow ...
I've got another question, Mrs Sharma!
Please, Mrs Sharma!
Look at the camera, Mrs Sharma!
Over here, Mrs Sharma!
Please, Mrs Sharma, what does it feel like to have saved the world?
But now she's famous all over the world.
Oh, I didn't do it all on my own. I had lots of help from my wonderful staff ... and two of my students. Now, I'm afraid I must get on. If you'd like an interview, speak to my secretary Mrs Jones ...

Everything seems quiet in here ...
But wait ... what's that high up in the sky?
UMMMMMMMMMMMMMMMM
Could it be ...?

CHAT ABOUT THE BOOK

1 How did Jamie and Verna get into the control room at the beginning of the story?

2 Go to page 43. Which word means the same as 'amazing'?

3 Read page 44. What did Ripley mean when she said, 'Look's like there's a storm coming'?

4 Go to page 33. 'Sharma. It's S-H-A-R-M-A. Mrs Sharma.' Why has the author written this line like this?

5 Three large pictures are used on pages 46 and 47. What effect do these have?

6 Re-read pages 19–22. What do you learn about Murlak?

7 How are Director Keller and Mrs Sharma similar?

8 If you were going to interview one of the characters, what questions would you ask and why?